This Book Belongs To:

_____

THE RAND McNALLY BOOK OF
Favorite Mother Goose Rhymes

Illustrated by ANNE SELLERS LEAF

RAND McNALLY & COMPANY Chicago

Established 1856

CONTENTS

THIS IS the house that Jack built.

This is the malt
That lay in the house that Jack
built.

This is the rat,
That ate the malt
That lay in the house that Jack
built.

This is the cat,
That killed the rat,
That ate the malt
That lay in the house that Jack
    built.

This is the dog,
That worried the cat,
That killed the rat,
That ate the malt
That lay in the house that Jack
built.

This is the cow with the crumpled
  horn,
That tossed the dog,
That worried the cat,
That killed the rat,
That ate the malt
That lay in the house that Jack
  built.

This is the maiden all forlorn,
That milked the cow with the
    crumpled horn,
That tossed the dog,
That worried the cat,
That killed the rat,
That ate the malt
That lay in the house that Jack
    built.

This is the man all tattered and
    torn,
That kissed the maiden all forlorn,
That milked the cow with the
    crumpled horn,
That tossed the dog,
That worried the cat,
That killed the rat,
That ate the malt
That lay in the house that Jack
    built.

This is the priest all shaven
  and shorn,
That married the man all
  tattered and torn,
That kissed the maiden all forlorn,
That milked the cow with the
  crumpled horn,
That tossed the dog,
That worried the cat,
That killed the rat,
That ate the malt
That lay in the house that Jack
  built.

This is the cock that crowed in
the morn,
That waked the priest all
shaven and shorn,
That married the man all
tattered and torn,
That kissed the maiden all forlorn,

That milked the cow with the
crumpled horn,
That tossed the dog,
That worried the cat,
That killed the rat,
That ate the malt
That lay in the house that Jack
built.

This is the farmer sowing the
corn,
That kept the cock that crowed
in the morn,
That waked the priest all
shaven and shorn,
That married the man all
tattered and torn,
That kissed the maiden all forlorn,

That milked the cow with the crumpled horn,
That tossed the dog,
That worried the cat,
That killed the rat,
That ate the malt
That lay in the house that Jack built.

JACK AND JILL

Jack and Jill went up the hill,
To fetch a pail of water;
Jack fell down, and broke his crown,
And Jill came tumbling after.

Then up Jack got and off did trot,
As fast as he could caper,
To old Dame Dob, who patched his nob
With vinegar and brown paper.

PUSSYCAT AND QUEEN

"Pussycat, pussycat,
    Where have you been?"
"I've been to London
    To look at the Queen."

"Pussycat, pussycat,
    What did you there?"
"I frightened a little mouse
    Under the chair."

HARK, HARK!

Hark, hark! the dogs do bark!
Beggars are coming to town:
Some in jags, and some in rags,
And some in velvet gown.

GOOSEY, GOOSEY, GANDER

"Goosey, Goosey, Gander,
    Whither dost thou wander?"
"Upstairs and downstairs
    And in my lady's chamber.

"There I met an old man
    Who wouldn't say his prayers;
I took him by the left leg,
    And threw him down the stairs."

CROSSPATCH

Crosspatch, draw the latch,
    Sit by the fire and spin;
Take a cup and drink it up,
    Then call your neighbors in.

PUSSYCAT BY THE FIRE

Pussycat sits by the fire;
How can she be fair?
In walks the little dog;
Says: "Pussy, are you there?
How do you do, Mistress Pussy?
Mistress Pussy, how d'ye do?"
"I thank you kindly, little dog,
I fare as well as you!"

A WEEK OF BIRTHDAYS

Monday's child is fair of face,
Tuesday's child is full of grace,
Wednesday's child is full of woe,
Thursday's child has far to go,
Friday's child is loving and giving,
Saturday's child works hard for
     its living;
But the child that's born on the
     Sabbath day
Is bonny and blithe, and good and gay.

ROCK-A-BYE, BABY

Rock-a-bye, baby, thy cradle is green;
Father's a nobleman, mother's a queen;
And Betty's a lady, and wears a gold
    ring,
And Johnny's a drummer, and drums
    for the king.

THE HOBBYHORSE

I had a little hobbyhorse,
 And it was dapple gray;
Its head was made of pea-straw,
 Its tail was made of hay.

I sold it to an old woman
 For a copper groat;
And I'll not sing my song again
 Without another coat.

GOING TO ST. IVES

As I was going to St. Ives
I met a man with seven wives.
Every wife had seven sacks,
Every sack had seven cats,
Every cat had seven kits.
Kits, cats, sacks, and wives,
How many were going to St. Ives?

THE WOMAN OF EXETER

There dwelt an old woman at Exeter;
When visitors came it sore vexed her,
So for fear they should eat,
She locked up all her meat,
This stingy old woman of Exeter.

THE KING OF FRANCE

The King of France went up the
hill,
With twenty thousand men;
The King of France came down the
hill,
And ne'er went up again.

WHAT ARE LITTLE BOYS MADE OF?

What are little boys made of,
  made of?
What are little boys made of?
"Snaps and snails, and puppy-dogs'
  tails;
And that's what little boys are
  made of."

What are little girls made of,
made of?
What are little girls made of?
"Sugar and spice, and all that's
nice;
And that's what little girls are
made of."

THE DONKEY

Donkey, donkey, old and gray,
Ope your mouth and gently bray;
Lift your ears and blow your horn,
To wake the world this sleepy morn.

THE OLD WOMAN OF LEEDS

There was an old woman of Leeds,
Who spent all her time in good
      deeds;
  She worked for the poor
  Till her fingers were sore,
This pious old woman of Leeds!

GOOD KING ARTHUR

When good King Arthur ruled this
    land,
    He was a goodly King;
He stole three pecks of barley meal,
    To make a bag-pudding.
A bag-pudding the King did make,
    And stuffed it well with plums,
And in it put great lumps of fat,
    As big as my two thumbs.
The King and Queen did eat thereof,
    And noblemen beside;
And what they could not eat that
    night,
    The Queen next morning fried.

BOY AND THE SPARROW

A little cock-sparrow sat on a green
tree,
And he chirruped, he chirruped, so
merry was he;
A naughty boy came with his wee
bow and arrow,
Determined to shoot this little cock-
sparrow.

"This little cock-sparrow shall make
me a stew,
And his giblets shall make me a
little pie, too."
"Oh, no," says the sparrow, "I won't
make a stew."
So he flapped his wings and away
he flew.

THE LION AND THE UNICORN

The Lion and the Unicorn were
fighting for the crown,
The Lion beat the Unicorn all
around the town.
Some gave them white bread, and
some gave them brown,
Some gave them plumcake, and
sent them out of town.

the winner!

LITTLE BOY BLUE

Little Boy Blue, come, blow your horn!
The sheep's in the meadow, the cow's in the corn.
Where's the little boy that looks after the sheep?
Under the haystack, fast asleep!

JACK

Jack be nimble,
Jack be quick,
Jack jump over
the candlestick.

COCK-CROW

Cocks crow in the morn
    To tell us to rise,
And he who lies late
    Will never be wise.
For early to bed
    And early to rise,
Is the way to be healthy
    And wealthy and wise.

THREE WISE MEN
OF GOTHAM

Three wise men of Gotham
Went to sea in a bowl,
If the bowl had been stronger
My song had been longer.

THE HUNTER OF REIGATE

A man went a-hunting at Reigate,
And wished to leap over a high gate.
　Says the owner, "Go round,
　With your gun and your hound,
For you never shall leap over my gate."

GEORGY PORGY

Georgy Porgy, pudding and pie,
Kissed the girls and made them cry.
When the boys came out to play,
Georgy Porgy ran away.

DOCTOR FOSTER

Doctor Foster went to Glo'ster,
In a shower of rain,
He stepped in a puddle up to his
middle,
And never went there again.

DIDDLE DIDDLE DUMPLING

Diddle diddle dumpling, my son John
Went to bed with his breeches on,
One stocking off, and one stocking on,
Diddle diddle dumpling, my son John.

MASTER I HAVE

Master I have, and I am his man,
    Gallop a dreary dun,
Master I have, and I am his man,
And I'll get a wife as fast as
      I can,
With a heighty gaily gamberally,
Higgledy piggledy, niggledy,
      niggledy,
    Gallop a dreary dun.

BLUE BELL BOY

I had a little boy,
  And called him Blue Bell,
Gave him a little work—
  He did it very well.

I bade him go upstairs
  To bring me a gold pin,
In coal scuttle fell he,
  Up to his little chin.

He went to the garden
To pick a little sage,
He tumbled on his nose,
And fell into a rage.

JACK JELF

Little Jack Jelf
Was put on the shelf
Because he could not spell "pie."
    When his aunt, Mrs. Grace,
    Saw his sorrowful face,
She could not help saying, "Oh, fie!"

And since Master Jelf
Was put on the shelf
Because he could not spell "pie,"
    Let him stand there so grim,
    And no more about him,
For I wish him a very good-by!

HANDY PANDY

Handy Pandy, Jack-a-dandy,
Loves plum cake and sugar candy,
He bought some at a grocer's shop,
And out he came, hop, hop, hop!

I'LL TELL YOU A STORY

I'll tell you a story
About Jack-a-Nory,
And now my story's begun.
I'll tell you another
About his brother,
And now my story is done.

LITTLE KING BOGGEN

Little King Boggen, he built a fine
hall,
Pie crust and pastry crust, that was
the wall,
The windows were made of black
puddings and white,
And slated with pancakes—you
ne'er saw the like!

TOMMY TITTLEMOUSE

Little Tommy Tittlemouse
Lived in a little house,
He caught fishes
In other men's ditches.

BOBBY SNOOKS

Little Bobby Snooks was fond of
    his books,
    And loved by his usher and master,
But naughty Jack Spry, he got a
    black eye,
    And carries his nose in a plaster.

POOR OLD ROBINSON CRUSOE!

Poor old Robinson Crusoe!
Poor old Robinson Crusoe!
They made him a coat
Of an old Nanny goat,
I wonder why they should do so!
With a ring-a-ting-tang,
And a ring-a-ting-tang,
Poor old Robinson Crusoe!

DAPPLE-GRAY

I had a little pony,
    His name was Dapple-Gray,
I lent him to a lady,
    To ride a mile away.

She whipped him, she slashed him,
    She rode him through the mire,
I would not lend my pony now
    For all the lady's hire.

THE KILKENNY CATS

There were once two cats
    of Kilkenny,
Each thought there was one cat
    too many.
So they fought and they fit,
And they scratched and they bit,
    Till, excepting their nails
    And the tips of their tails,
Instead of two cats, there
    weren't any.

CAESAR'S SONG

Bow-wow-wow!
Whose dog art thou?
Little Tom Tinker's dog,
Bow-wow-wow!

THE LITTLE BIRD

Once I saw a little bird
    Come hop, hop, hop,
So I cried, "Little bird,
    Will you stop, stop, stop?"

And was going to the window
    To say, "How do you do?"
But he shook his little tail,
    And far away he flew.

WILLY, WILLY

Willy, Willy Wilkin
Kissed the maids a-milking,
Fa, la, la!
And with his merry daffing
He set them all a-laughing,
Ha, ha, ha!

BANDY LEGS

As I was going to sell my eggs,
I met a man with bandy legs,
Bandy legs and crooked toes—
I tripped up his heels, and he
fell on his nose.

LITTLE FRED

When little Fred went to bed,
He always said his prayers,
He kissed mamma, and then papa,
And straightway went upstairs.

OLD
MOTHER
HUBBARD

Old Mother Hubbard
Went to the cupboard,
To give her poor dog a bone,

But when she got there
The cupboard was bare,
    And so the poor dog had none.

She went to the fishmonger's
To buy him some fish,

But when she came back
He was licking the dish.

She went to the hatter's
To buy him a hat,

When she came back
He was feeding the cat.

She went to the barber's
To buy him a wig,

When she came back
He was dancing a jig.

She went to the fruiterer's
To buy him some fruit,

When she came back
He was playing the flute.

She went to the tailor's
To buy him a coat,

When she came back
He was riding a goat.

She went to the cobbler's
To buy him some shoes,

When she came back
He was reading the news.

She went to the seamstress
To buy him some linen,

When she came back
The dog was a-spinning.

She went to the hosier's
To buy him some hose,

When she came back
He was dressed in his clothes.

The dame made a curtsy,
The dog made a bow,

The dame said, "Your servant,"
The dog said, "Bow-wow."

OLD KING COLE

Old King Cole
Was a merry old soul,
And a merry old soul was he.
He called for his pipe,
And he called for his bowl,
And he called for his fiddlers three!
And every fiddler, he had a fine
fiddle,

And a very fine fiddle had he.
"Twee tweedle dee, tweedle dee,"
went the fiddlers.
Oh, there's none so rare
As can compare
With King Cole and his fiddlers
three.

MARY, MARY, QUITE CONTRARY

Mary, Mary, quite contrary,
    How does your garden grow?
Silver bells and cockle-shells,
    And pretty maids all of a row.

LITTLE JACK HORNER

Little Jack Horner
Sat in a corner,
   Eating of Christmas pie.
He put in his thumb,
And pulled out a plum,
   And said, "What a good boy
     am I!"

THE MULBERRY BUSH

Here we go round the mulberry bush,
The mulberry bush, the mulberry
bush,
Here we go round the mulberry bush
On a cold and frosty morning.

LITTLE PUSSY

"I like little Pussy,
    Her coat is so warm,
And if I don't hurt her
    She'll do me no harm.
So I'll not pull her tail,
    Nor drive her away,
But Pussy and I
    Very gently will play."

COCK-A-DOODLE-DO!

Cock-a-doodle-do!
My dame has lost her shoe,
My master's lost his fiddle-stick
And knows not what to do.

Cock-a-doodle-do!
What is my dame to do?
Till master finds his fiddle-stick,
She'll dance without her shoe.

LITTLE BO-PEEP

Little Bo-Peep has lost her sheep,
And can't tell where to find
them.
Leave them alone, and they'll
come home,
And bring their tails behind
them.

HUMPTY DUMPTY

Humpty Dumpty sat on a wall,
Humpty Dumpty had a great fall.
All the King's horses, and all the
King's men
Cannot put Humpty Dumpty together
again.

THE MOUSE AND THE CLOCK

Hickory, dickory, dock!
The mouse ran up the clock,
The clock struck one,
And down he run,
Hickory, dickory, dock!

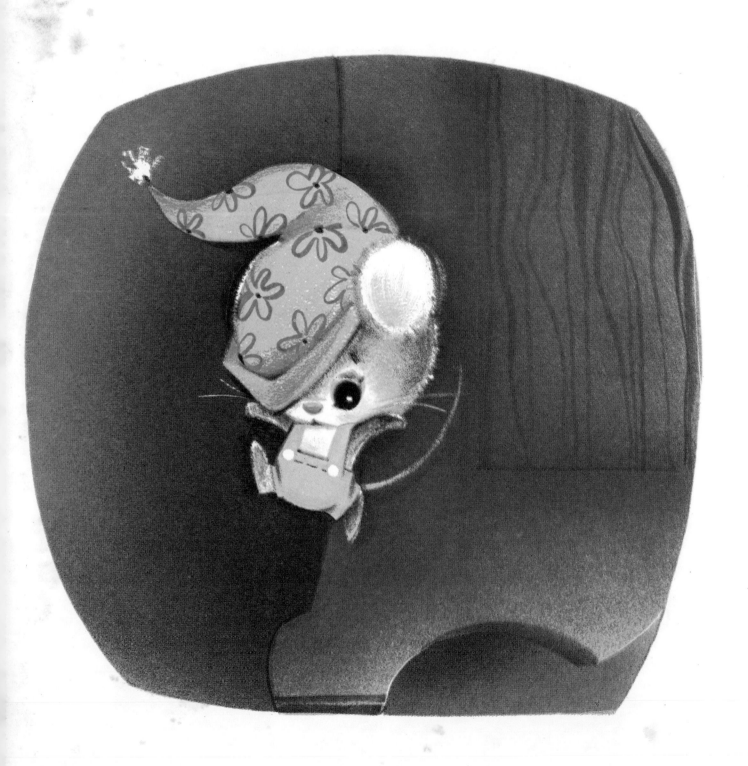